m people fresco

Exclusive Distributors:

Music Sales Limited
8/9 Frith Street,
London W1V 5TZ,
England.

Music Sales Pty Limited
120 Rothschild Avenue,
Rosebery, NSW 2018,
Australia.

Order No. AM953667
ISBN 0-7119-7164-1

Your Guarantee of Quality:
As publishers, we strive to
produce every book to the highest
commercial standards.
The music has been freshly
engraved and, whilst endeavouring
to retain the original running order
of the recorded album, the book has
been carefully designed to minimise
awkward page turns and to make
playing from it a real pleasure.

Particular care has been given
to specifying acid-free, neutral-sized
paper made from pulps which
have not been elemental chlorine
bleached.
This pulp is from farmed
sustainable forests and was
produced with special regard
for the environment.
Throughout, the printing
and binding have been planned
to ensure a sturdy, attractive
publication which should give
years of enjoyment.
If your copy fails to meet our
high standards, please inform us
and we will gladly replace it.

Music arranged by Derek Jones.
Music processed by
Paul Ewers Music Design.

Printed in the United Kingdom by
Halstan & Co Limited, Amersham,
Buckinghamshire.

Music Sales' complete
catalogue describes thousands
of titles and is available in full colour
sections by subject, direct from
Music Sales Limited.
Please state your areas of
interest and send a cheque/postal
order for £1.50 for postage to:
Music Sales Limited,
Newmarket Road,
Bury St. Edmunds, Suffolk IP33 3YB.

Wise Publications
London / New York / Paris / Sydney / Copenhagen / Madrid

C000160865

just for you

Words & Music by Mike Pickering, Paul Heard & Heather Small

gold and sil - ver to your door   just for___ you.___   I will raise my glass___ up to   the sky

just for you.___   I will   be your strength___ and be   a pride,___   be   with___ you._____

2. I'll make

sweet soul mu - sic all_ night long___   just for you.___   Make you feel_ that you be - long___
(Verse 3 see block lyric)

Verse 3:
I'll be a shooting star in the sky at night
Just for you
I'll be a mother of pearl, diamond bright
Just for you
I'll lock the door, throw away the key
Just for you
I am the air that you breathe
I am you.

Just for you I'll wash *etc.*

fantasy island

Words & Music by Mike Pickering, Paul Heard & Heather Small

1. Gath-er round peo-ple I just dreamt of this song, a-bout all the world___ get-
(Verse 2 see block lyric)

This is my fan - ta - sy.—

This is my fan - ta - sy.—

This is my fan - ta - sy.—

My fan - ta - sy.

My fan - ta - sy

And dream with me ba - by.

Say

what have we got,___ we got the pow - er.___ Got six - ty sec-onds, got ev - ery

hour.___ Say what have we got,___ we got the pow - er.___ We

are the spark___ to light the fire.___ Got one blood, got one skin, got one

soul deep with - in. Got a heart beat-ing fast, got a dream, got no past. Say

D.%. al Coda

this is— my, this is— my fan - ta - sy.—

⊕ *Coda*

Repeat ad lib. to fade

Instrumental solo

Verse 2:
There's a welcome mat at the centre of the earth
No sign of hate, a four letter word
The children are playing in air you can breath
People got dreams, people achieve
Everywhere's music, sunshine and laughter
We still feel the same the morning after
Words in the air, love in the heart
This is my dream, a brand new start.

This is my island *etc.*

never mind love

Words & Music by Mike Pickering, Paul Heard & Heather Small

1. I played out this scene be-fore too ma-ny ___ times. ___
(Verse 2 see block lyric)
I

walked a-cross ___ the crowd-ed room and looked him in ___ the eye.

Verse 2:
How you gonna change the habit of a lifetime overnight?
You think you're so immortal, so eternal, out of sight
The questions I am gonna ask aren't the ones you wanna hear
Alone inside your narrow mind, now let's get one thing clear
Unlike Sinatra you ain't under my skin
What can I tell ya, don't know where to begin
Can't find your heart now, but who's lookin' anyway
Hasta luego, adios, I'm on my way.

Never mind *etc.*

last night 10,000

Words & Music by Mike Pickering, Paul Heard & Heather Small

don't look my way you know I'm bad news.___ Feel the tears

on my cheek,___ a - buse me now 'cos I've got to eat.___

Where was last night, I for - get. This

ain't no big is - sue it's just life___ and death. Last night___ ten thou - sand___

out in— the rain,_____ bel - low - ing si - lence.

May - be— it's now or nev - er a - gain._____

Spoken: I'll do anything to forget, after all, what is there left? But in the black of night   frosty stars and vice.

26

I'm too old to learn,   too young to turn.   And as you walk by with ghosts in your eyes the world still turns.

Instrumental solo

D.%. al Coda

✠ *Coda*

Instrumental solo ad lib.

Repeat ad lib. to fade

Verse 2:
Eyes are down, looking in
I'm sorry but I'm not on your screen
I hold a cup in my hand
To help me reach my own promised land
Crown of thorns on my head
Wrapped up in my own cardboard bed
I got youth by my side
A victim of your crime, nothing to hide.

Last night ten thousand *etc.*

smile

Words & Music by Mike Pickering, Paul Heard & Heather Small

A kiss to wipe away the tears, can't keep on push-in' back the years.

We gave up this thing long a-go just like the stream for-ev-er flows.

This ain't de-vo-tion and it's not de-feat, I'm trapped in a kitch-en, can't stand the heat.

Like tears fall-ing from a wound-ed sky, let's leave it here, it's time to say good-

Verse 2:
Would it make you happy if I said I cared for you?
Spread my warmth around you in the cold night air
Walk with me up to the edge looking over at our life ahead
I may seem a fool to you in everything I say or do.
But I know this is our fate
I think we've past the sell by date
The encore's through, the show's at an end
Consign me to history but stay my friend.

You're not man *etc.*

lonely

Words & Music by Mike Pickering, Paul Heard & Heather Small

33

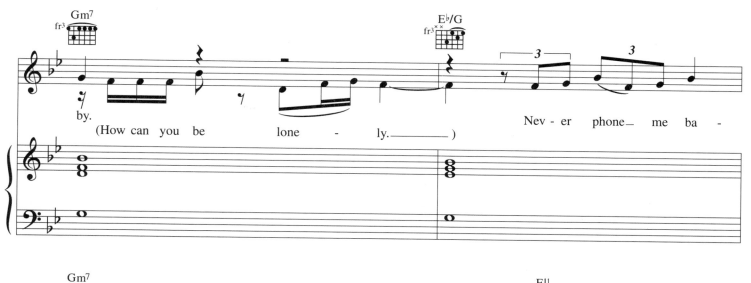

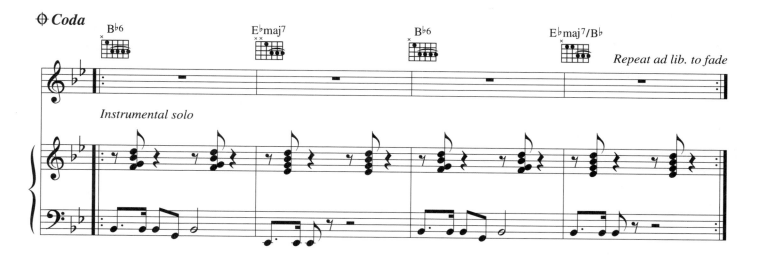

D.%. al Coda

Repeat ad lib. to fade

Instrumental solo

Verse 2:
In a life striving to survive
You are my guiding light
Like fruit on a tree and the air we breathe
You are my freedom, my strength inside
Oh yeah such joy.

No other feeling *etc.*

red flower sunset

Words & Music by Mike Pickering, Paul Heard & Heather Small

spring and sum-mer, au - tumn, win - ter, my all - time won-der man._

(Verse 2 see block lyric)

This mo-ment in love_ that_ we share_ could on-ly

be_ the pre-sent tense._ My foun-tain of hope,_ my gold-

-en sun,_ you are_ my great_ North Star._ The

one   red___ flow-er sun - set,   my   red___ flow-er sun-

- set.   Ba-by how   I___ a - dore___ it,

my   red___ flow-er sun - set.

2. For

My__ red__ flow-er sun - set.   (Talk-in' 'bout my   (Da   da__ da da.__

Repeat ad lib. to end

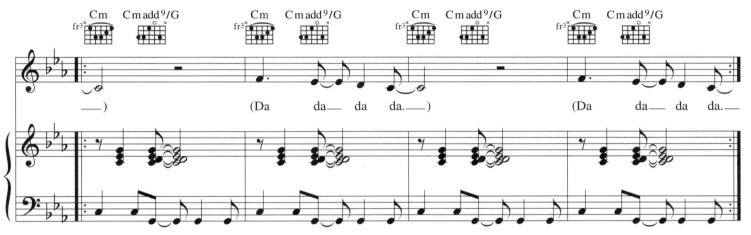

__)   (Da   da__ da da.__)   (Da   da__ da da.__

Verse 2:
For us there's no such thing as time
Just a moment forever
Holding me in your arms so tight
You know I feel out of this world
A miracle in modern times
That's you and me I swear to God
A celebration symphony
Played out by angels from above
Like the sands of time or a moment's beat
I don't really mind
'Cos I'm right here, eyes open wide
Staring back into our…

One red flower sunset *etc.*

angel st

Words & Music by Mike Pickering, Paul Heard & Heather Small

1. If you think the world owes you a ride you'll nev-er find the rea-son why.

(Verse 2 see block lyric)

So what have you got to lose?

An - gel Street, stand on your own two feet, 'cos ba-by

can't you see if we're to stay a-live on-ly the strong sur-vive.

2. Don't you know

Verse 2:
Don't you know if you can't respect yourself
You'll be left on the shelf
No one's gonna carry you.
Walkin' tall, dreaming of love and pride
Reachin' up to the sky
Arms and eyes are open wide
So come on let's climb the stair out of this
Make a wish, steal a kiss
Boy what have you got to lose?

Angel Street *etc.*

rhythm and blues

Words & Music by Mike Pickering, Paul Heard & Heather Small

(The sun shines in our eyes, my skin in a dif - ferent dis - guise.)

Verse 2:
Down in the ghetto, marking time with self-belief
Babylon voices, square-eyed dreams of dignity
Feeling the pressure, searching for another place
Lift up our voices, use our minds, we will be released.

Breakin' out of the skin *etc.*

believe it

Words & Music by Mike Pickering, Paul Heard & Heather Small

Verse 2:
I looked at love on Channel Three
I just don't know who to believe
Johnny slapped her in the face
Turn the cheek, turn the page
Boombox plays, who gets the joke
I can't help wondering what's the dope
Goldfish bowl inside my head
Truth and lies hanging by a thread.

Can you believe it *etc.*